Useful books

The information books listed below are specifically written for young children. The text is clear and simple and the books contain illustrations and photographs of a high standard.

The stories and poems cover a range of understanding and reading ability, and provide useful starting-points for work on the senses.

Children's information books

Aliki, *My Five Senses,* Harper Collins.

Ballard, Carol, *How our Bodies Work* [four titles], Wayland.

Pluckrose, Henry, *Sense* [five titles], Franklin Watts.

Suhr, Mandy, and Gordon, Mike, *The Senses* [five titles], Wayland.

Walpole, Brenda, and Watts, Barrie, *See for Yourself* [four titles], A and C Black.

Children's stories and poems

Bennet, Jill, *Noisy Poems*, Open University Press.

Campbell, Rod, *Look Touch and Feel with Buster*, Campbell Books.

Carle, Eric, *The Very Quiet Cricket*, Hamish Hamilton.

Cole, Babette, *The Smelly Book*, Collins Picture Lions.

Fox, Neri, and Denton, Terry, *Night Noises*, Harcourt Brace Big Books.

Frost, Miriam, and Bolinger, Christine, *In The Chicken Coop*, T.W.G. Books.

Mackinnon, Debbie, and Steveking, Anthea, *What a Noise*, Francis Lincoln.

Murphy, Mary, *You Smell*, Dorling Kindersley.

Savage, Elizabeth, and Magnussen, Diana, *Grumbles Growls and Roars*, T.W.G. Books.

Williams, Rebel, and Howe, Phillip, *City Storm*, T.W.G. Books.

The books in this next section provide a selection of cross-curricular activities for 4–6 year olds. The further reading provides background information, with an emphasis on the importance of play in the Early Years classroom.

Teachers' books

Carratello, Patty and John, and Charon, Rick, *Let's Investigate the Senses*, Teacher Created Materials.

Howe, Linda, Collins Primary Science, *Our Senses*, Collins Educational.

Morrow, Jan, and Tushingham, Karen, *Science through the Senses*, Longman.

Nicholls, Sue, *Bobby Shaftoe, Clap Your Hands*, A and C Black.

Richards, Roy, and Collis, Margaret, *An Early Start to Science*, Macdonald Educational.

Styles, Morag, and Triggs, Pat, *Poetry 0-16*, B.F.K.

Further reading

Bruce, Tina, *Time to Play in Early Childhood Education*, Hodder and Stoughton.

Hall, Nigel, and Abbot, Lesley, [ed], *Play in the Early Years*, Hodder and Stoughton.

Harlen, Wynne, [ed], Primary Science, *Taking the Plunge*, Heinemann.

Jarvis, Tina, *Children and Primary Science*, Cassell.

Jelly, Sheila, and Harlen, Wynne, *Developing Science in the Primary Classroom*, Longman.

1 | Seeing

Learning outcomes

To understand

▶ That the eye works in conjunction with the brain

▶ That without light we cannot see.

To recognise

▶ That a mirror shows a reflection.

▶ The existence of optical illusions.

To develop ideas about

▶ Why sight is of primary importance.

▶ How living things have adapted their sense of sight in order to function in the environment.

Programme outline

The programme opens with a montage of eyes. We move to watch a doctor examine the outside and inside of the eye. Eyeful Ella helps us understand how light enters the eye, makes an inverted image on the retina and sends a message to the brain. By using binoculars we see how things seem really close, and how small things, like a woodlouse, look bigger under a magnifying glass. At the zoo we investigate how animals' eyes differ from our own, the position of the eyes, and whether they are used for day or night vision.

A visit to Gough's Cave shows how light, bouncing off walls and the children, enables us to see them. We travel to Bristol where children investigate mirrors and reflections, then return to the cave to examine reflections in water.

Next we see red, blue and green light reflected by a curved mirror to form white light. Children then discuss and react to a selection of optical illusions, including a mask of Charlie Chaplin. We then see an artist, using red, yellow and blue oil paint, together with white, to make all the other colours she will need for the painting of Teddy's tea party.

The programme ends by reminding us that if there is light we can see colour, shape and movement.

Before the programme

▶ Look at each other's eyes and talk about eyelashes, eyebrows and eyelids.

▶ Talk about wearing glasses and how important they are.

▶ Discuss any visits to an optician or an eye hospital that the children may have experienced.

▶ Discuss the words binoculars and magnifying glass and discuss what they do.

▶ Talk about blindness and how it might feel. How do the children feel about the dark?

Whilst watching

▶ Tell the children to watch out for Eyeful Ella and try to remember what she sees.

▶ Ask children to look out for all the different kinds of vision that animals can have.

Key vocabulary

Seeing, sight, eyeball, eyelash, iris, pupil, eyelid, retina, images, messages, light, mirror, reflection, beam, prism, camouflage, blind, glasses, lens, illusion.

Follow-up activities

▶ Set up an area in the classroom devoted to the senses. Start a collection of objects associated with sight.

▶ Give the children opportunities to investigate the properties of a variety of mirrors.

▶ Set up an optician's as part of structured play.

▶ Encourage the children's observational skills by drawing fruits, flowers or each other. Provide magnifying glasses to encourage close attention to detail.

▶ Ask the children to imagine they had a magic mirror and write a description of what they might see in their mirror.

▶ Make an eye montage with the class. Use pairs of eyes taken from newspapers and magazines for the collection.

▶ Discuss the things the children think are beautiful to look at. Encourage them to choose favourite book illustrations and pieces of art.

Activity sheet 1 – Mirror Images

By using a mirror with these pictures the children will develop an awareness of symmetry.

Activity sheet 2 – Make a Colour Spinner

This activity enables the children to see how colours mix together to make new colours.

Activity sheet 3 – I Spy

Children are given an opportunity to recall some of the objects in the programme. It is intended to help children discriminate initial letter sounds.

Mirror Images

Name_____

Use a mirror. Complete the pictures.

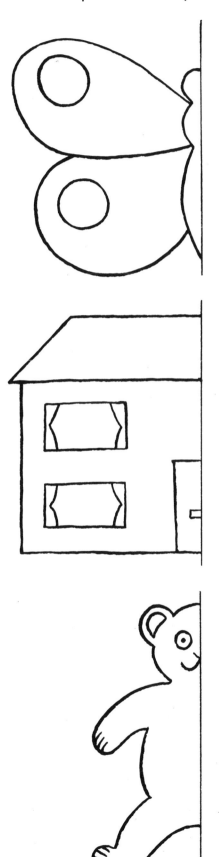

Make a colour spinner

Name

Colour each section a different colour.

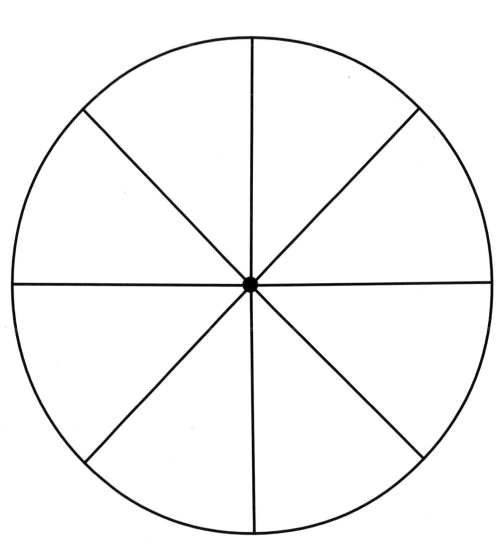

Push a pencil through the centre. Now spin.

I Spy

Name_____

I spy with my little eye, something beginning with...

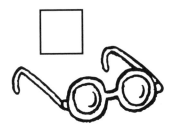

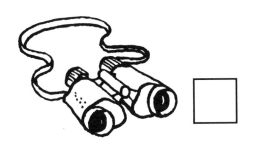

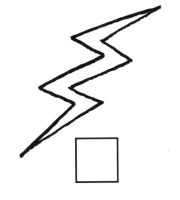

2 | Hearing

Learning outcomes

To understand

▶ That the ear works in conjunction with the brain.

▶ That sound comes from vibrating objects.

To recognise

▶ The existence of sound waves, which are invisible.

▶ That we hear sounds all the time.

To develop ideas about

▶ How sounds can conjure moods and images.

▶ How the sense of hearing can compensate for the loss of sight.

Programme outline

The programme opens with a number of different animals making sounds and people and animals listening. We then move to Gough's cave, near Cheddar Gorge, where a group of children identify sounds they can hear by playing the 'listening game'.

Next we visit a hospital where a doctor is shown examining Jamal's ear. A diagram helps to explain how sound enters the ear and how messages are carried back to the brain.

The way in which some animals are specially adapted for hearing is illustrated by observing an elephant, a cricket and an owl at the zoo.

Bob Smart and some children visit Gough's Cave and find out that hearing doesn't just depend on your ears, but also on where you are – sound can do strange things in caves.

The children and Bob see horseshoe bats, and find out that bats use echoes and have excellent hearing.

In a sound studio a group of children pretend to be ghosts and make their own ghost noises. They are encouraged to identify atmosphere soundtracks from a computer.

Before the programme

▶ Discuss children's ear problems and any experience they have had of visits to the doctor or hospital.

▶ Discuss deafness and how it may feel.

▶ Emphasise the importance of listening.

▶ Look at musical instruments and the sounds they make. Can the children make their own musical sounds such as clapping hands and whistling?

▶ Look at pictures and diagrams of ears.

▶ Discuss the connection between sound and mood.

▶ Talk about the different sounds that animals make.

Whilst watching

Remind the children to look out for Noisy Ned and remember what he does. Ask the children to try and notice as many sounds as they can. Suggest that they pick out the sound they like best, such as the birds singing or water rippling.

Key vocabulary

hearing, hear, studio, echoes, whispers, silence, soundtrack, eardrum, wax, outer, middle, inner, sound waves, nerve, mood, tuning fork.

Follow-up activities

▶ Build up the sense area by adding pictures of ears and musical instruments. Add to the vocabulary bank.

▶ Look at and collect pictures of different animal ears. Then make some different-sized and -shaped ears such as cones or large flaps. Try out and discuss results.

▶ Make a display of musical instruments and set a number of challenges for the children such as making the sound of raindrops falling or a crocodile snapping.

▶ Ask the children to design and make an instrument to shake, pluck, strike or blow.

▶ Explore vibrations with the class. Place a handful of rice on a drum and ask the children to observe what happens if the drum is banged; or suggest they hold a balloon close to a playing radio and watch how the balloon reacts.

▶ Try pouring water or rustling paper and encourage the children to brainstorm all the words that describe these sounds. Shape them into a poem.

▶ Play Chinese whispers.

▶ Listen to music such as The Carnival of the Animals. Ask the children to respond to the mood and dynamics of the piece either in dance or through painting.

▶ Working in pairs or as a whole class try making sounds over different distances. Discuss results.

Activity sheet 4 – Animal Sounds

This sheet helps children identify the sounds animals make. The matching activity encourages left to right orientation.

Activity sheet 5 – We Can Hear...

This activity will promote the children's listening skills and draw their attention to the variety of sounds around them.

Activity sheet 6 – Sounds Like...

The children will develop an understanding of how sounds can be grouped and categorised.

Animal Sounds

Name _____

Can you match each animal to its sound?

quack

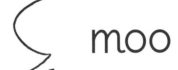
moo

miaow

woof

baa

We Can Hear...

Name_____

Sounds we heard

Inside	Outside

STOP, LOOK, LISTEN THE SENSATIONS

Sounds Like...

Name _____

Which of these sound alike? Match the pictures.

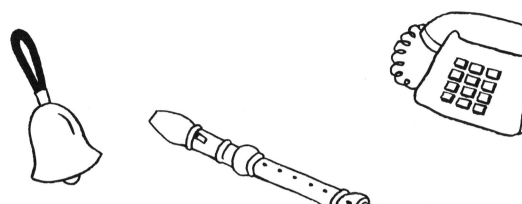

3 | Smelling

Learning outcomes

To understand

▶ That the nose works in conjunction with the brain.

▶ That smells are invisible and float in the air.

To recognise

▶ That almost everything has a smell and smells can be natural or manufactured.

▶ That smells can protect us from danger.

▶ That sense of smell is very important for many animals.

To develop ideas about

▶ The variety of smells around us and our reactions to them.

Programme outline

The programme opens with people and animals sniffing a range of everyday smells. This is followed by a doctor looking at Alice's nose. Through a diagram it is explained that smells that are floating in the air go up to the top of our noses where there are lots of little nerve endings. These nerve endings then take a message about the smell to the brain.

We next visit Dr George Dodd, an expert on smells. He visits a school where the children experience a great variety of smells, both pleasant and unpleasant and make comments. We also see Dr Dodd and the children out by a loch noticing the great variety of natural smells around them.

At the zoo we then see sloth bears, a rhino, elephants and a little furry creature called a coati.

The programme concludes with a visit to the Highlands of Scotland where we meet Max, a search and rescue dog. Max and the ranger Seamus McNally demonstrate how someone who is lost in the mountains can be found because of the scent they leave behind.

Before the programme

▶ Identify smelling as one of the senses which gives us information about the world around us.

▶ Look at different shapes and sizes of noses and discuss smells we like and dislike. Talk about problems which could hinder our sense of smell, such as a cold.

▶ Think about how smells may warn us of danger and emphasise the need for safety when smelling things.

▶ Talk about how we use dogs to help us because of their sense of smell.

Whilst watching

▶ Ask the children to look out for Smelly Sam and to remember what he does.

▶ Ask the children to try and remember as many of the nice and nasty smells as they can.

Key vocabulary

smell, smelling, perfume, scent, natural, manufactured.

Follow-up activities

▶ Add a collection of scented items to your sensory area such as potpourri, spices, and fresh fruit. Build up the vocabulary bank.

▶ Collect a range of things which have a strong smell such as coffee, mint and vinegar. Put a little of each into a plastic cup and cover with tissue paper. The children then guess the contents of each cup. Extend this activity by having pairs of smells which the children have to match up.

▶ Make a class collection of favourite smells. Choose five or six smells and record on a block graph the favourite smells chosen by the class.

▶ Collect together pictures of things that smell. Ask the children to sort them into sets using given criteria or categories of their own.

▶ Make a list of places such as the garden, supermarket and the swimming-baths. Ask the children to describe how these places smell.

▶ Make a smelly book. Children add pictures and words to record their experiences of smelling.

▶ Read Babette Cole's *The Smelly Book* to the children, who can then be asked to write their own smelly poem or story.

▶ Make a list of smells from around school.

Activity sheet 7 – Help Max...

Sense of smell is very important to some animals. This activity helps children recognize this as well as developing pencil skills.

Activity sheet 8 – Different Smells

This activity develops the idea of the wide variety of smells around us and our reaction to them. The children have to sort using their own criteria.

Activity sheet 9 – My Potpourri

This activity guides the children through the process of designing, making and evaluating their own potpourri.

Help Max...

Name _____

Help Max find the climber and take him to hospital.

STOP, LOOK, LISTEN   THE SENSATIONS   © 1998 CHANNEL FOUR LEARNING LIMITED

Name _____

Different Smells

Cut out these pictures and sort them into sets.
See if your friend can guess how you did it.

14

STOP, LOOK, LISTEN THE SENSATIONS

4 SCHOOLS

My Potpourri

Name _____

I will use...

This is what I will do...

Now I've finished...

This is what I like...

Next time I might...

4 Tasting

Learning outcomes

To understand

▶ That taste and smell are closely linked.

▶ That there are four categories – sweet, salty, bitter and sour – and these are tasted on different parts of the tongue.

To recognize

▶ That flavour is usually a mixture of two or more of these categories.

▶ That we need food for energy and like to eat food that tastes good.

To develop ideas about

▶ The variety of tastes available to us and our reactions to them.

Programme outline

The programme opens with animals feeding, licking and preening and food being eaten. We then see a great variety of foods at the supermarket and how meals are a mixture of different foods.

Next we visit a hospital where a doctor examines Alice's tongue. Through a diagram we find out that we taste food with our tongue and that tastebuds sense if something is sweet, salty, sour or bitter and a message is sent to the brain.

We then join chef John Dicken and a group of children who are helping him for the day. The children learn that taste is the most important sense, along with smell, when cooking. They identify the taste of specially prepared samples.

A visit to the zoo allows us to see the favourite food of some of the animals, including the giraffe, the kinkajou (from South America), a sloth bear and her cub, cows and a fly.

We return to the kitchen and find out that we taste with different parts of our tongue. Next John and the children prepare a meal, seasoning and tasting as they go and discussing which flavours go together and which do not.

The programme ends when the children serve a meal to two adults in a restaurant, reminding us that smell and taste work closely together.

Before the programme

▶ Introduce the four different categories of taste and explain the different areas of the tongue where we taste these.

▶ Introduce the concept of taste buds and explain that there are thousands of them.

▶ Discuss the link between taste and smell.

▶ Think about preparing and eating food and talk about tastes we like and don't like. Explain the need for safety when tasting things and emphasise how important this is.

Whilst watching

▶ Tell the children to look out for Tasty Tessa and try to remember what she does.

▶ Ask the children which of the foods seen in the programme they have tasted before, and which they would like to taste.

Key vocabulary

taste, tasting, tongue, sweet, bitter, salty, sour, flavour, energy, taste buds, saliva, seasoning.

Follow-up activities

▶ Extend your sense area with more objects and vocabulary.

▶ Take a bag of shopping to school and let the children taste the items. Make a pictogram showing food they like and food they don't like.

▶ Ask the children to sort and classify items or pictures of food.

▶ Provide an opportunity for children to try the apple and potato test. Can they tell which they are tasting with their nose held? Discuss how our sense of taste and our sense of smell work together.

▶ Crisps come in lots of flavours. Can the children match the taste to the crisp packet?

▶ Try mixing drinks or jellies with food colouring. Can the children still identify the flavour?

▶ Have a class picnic. Ask the children to bring something they enjoy to share with one another.

▶ Make up a story about a magic cake or drink. What happens when you taste it?

▶ Make up, and try out, a recipe for a fruit yoghurt or drink.

Activity sheet 10 – My Favourite Meal

This sheet helps the children to recognise that we like to eat food that tastes good. Compare the foods chosen by each child.

Activity sheet 11 – Label the Tongue

The children should understand that there are different parts of the tongue. They can label these on the activity sheet.

Activity sheet 12 – Tastes Like...

This activity should help the children to understand that food can be categorised into four main groups: sweet, sour, salty and bitter.

My Favourite Meal

Name _____

Plan your favourite meal. Which tastes do you like best?

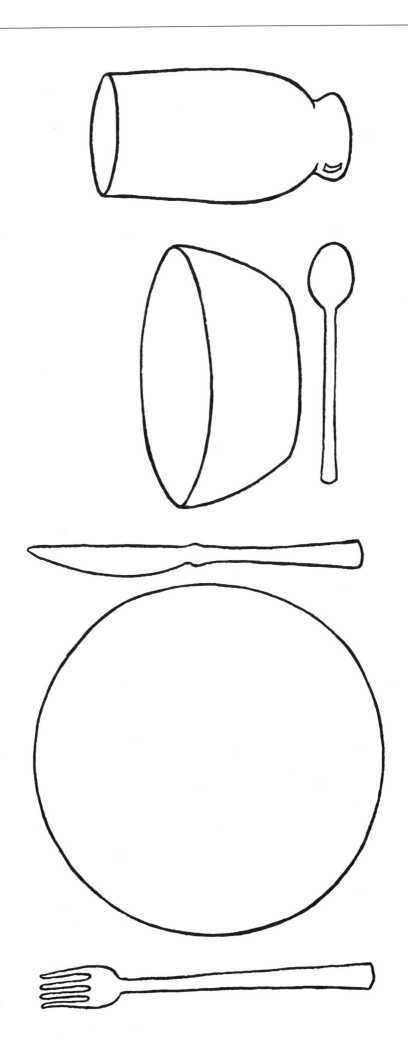

Label the Tongue

Name_____

Can you write the labels on the tongue?

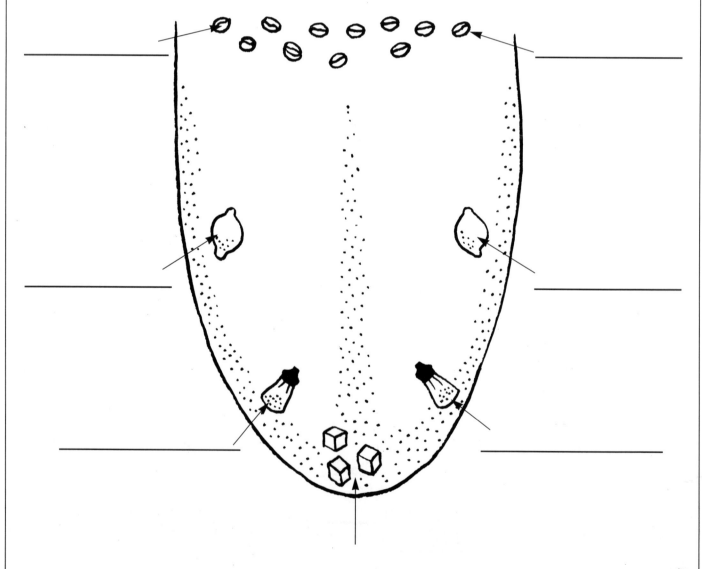

coffee   bitter

lemon   sour

salt   salty

sugar   sweet

STOP, LOOK, LISTEN THE SENSATIONS

Tastes Like...

Name _____

Draw these foods in the correct box.

crisps   **lemon**   **honey**   **coffee**

sweet	salty
bitter	**sour**

Now draw some more food in each box.

5 | Touching

Learning outcomes

To understand

▶ That the sense of touch works in conjunction with the brain.

▶ That we feel with the whole of our body.

▶ That some parts are more sensitive than others.

To recognise

▶ That messages to the brain can get confused.

▶ That we feel through our skin.

To develop ideas about

▶ The importance of the sense of touch for humans and animals.

Programme outline

After the introductory montage of children touching and feeling animals, we move into a classroom. Children describe and react to objects in a feely box. Next John Wiltshire, the blind piano tuner, shows how he uses his sense of touch to read braille by feeling the dots.

At the hospital the doctor shows how we feel with different parts of our skin, cheek, fingers and forearm. A diagram shows how a message is sent from a nerve in the toe to the brain.

At the zoo we look at hair on the elephant, whiskers on the tiger and what the cockroach uses to touch.

A snapshot of how the body feels at bathtime leads into an explanation of a physiotherapist's work. We see Sue Whitby at work when she visits Robert, Kelly and Rachel at their school.

Next we move to the playground, we see children playing on different kinds of surfaces.

The programme ends with John Wiltshire feeling his way to the pelican crossing with the help of Duke, his guide dog. John feels the bumps in the pavement through his shoes and they can safely cross the road.

Before the programme

▶ Discuss different ways we touch and feel including appropriate and inappropriate touch.

▶ Encourage the children to touch things with fingers, toes and against the face. Which part of the body is it easiest to feel with?

▶ Think about pleasant and unpleasant sensations.

Whilst watching

▶ Remind the children to look out for Feely Fred and try to remember what he does.

▶ Point out to children how the sense of touch can be helpful. Ask them to look for examples in the programme, e.g. animals preening, physiotherapy.

Key vocabulary

touch, touching, texture, pain, smooth, rough, spiky, slimy, tepid, hot, cold, wet, dry, massage, skin, nerves.

Follow-up activities

▶ Complete your sensory area and vocabulary bank.

▶ Make a collection of the children's fingerprints. Stress to each child the uniqueness of their fingerprints.

▶ Make a variety of printed pictures and patterns. How many different textures can the children create?

▶ Make a feely wall using a variety of craft/scrap materials such as wool, sawdust, feathers and beads.

▶ Make a feely box. Change the object in the box each day. Try to offer the children as many different shapes and textures as possible.

▶ Experiment with clay or modelling material. Collect things such as sticks, leaves, shells and marbles that the children can press in the clay to create different textures.

▶ Ask the children to write their name or initials in seeds, grains or wool.

▶ Provide the children with dried foods which they can add to the sand tray to create different textures.

▶ Play around with words. Support the class in finding adjectives, opposites and synonyms all to do with our sense of touch.

▶ Let the children time themselves doing simple activities such as threading beads or building with bricks, once with a pair of gloves on, and once without.

Activity sheet 13 – Picture This

This activity introduces the words smooth, rough, hard, soft, slippery and sticky to describe the feel of different objects.

Activity sheet 14 – The Hot and Cold Touch Test

This test enables the children to recognise how messages to the brain can sometimes get confused.

Activity sheet 15 – Feels Like...

This activity develops the idea that all things have a texture. Animal coats and skins provide a good example of this.

Picture This

Name _____

Draw a picture of something that feels...

smooth		rough		hard	

sticky		slippery		soft	

21

The Hot and Cold Touch Test

Name _____

| use your left hand | very warm water | Then... | lukewarm water | Write here how your hand felt. |
| use your right hand | cold water | Then... | lukewarm water | Write here how your hand felt. |

Feels Like...

Name _____

Choose the right word

spiky   **rough**   **sticky**   **furry**   **smooth**

I am
_____

I am
_____

I am
_____

I am
_____

I am
_____

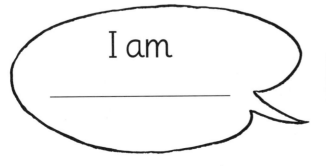

The Five Senses

Name_____

Match the words with the pictures.

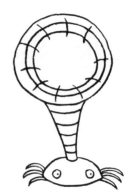

tongue

skin

nose

ear

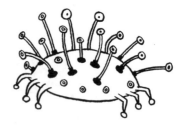

eye

STOP, LOOK, LISTEN THE SENSATIONS